The Village Tree

story and pictures

BY TARO YASHIMA

Taro Yashima is a Japanese who has been living in America since before the war. Recently his little daughter Momo has been asking him for stories about his childhood.

For Taro Yashima the center of his youth was the huge village tree which stood on the bank of the river. Here in the summer sun the children scrambled in the branches, jumped into the river, swam and tumbled, and played on the beach.

Very simply and freshly, Mr. Yashima has captured the wonder of being young, in any village, or in any country. The freedom and curiosity of the children, and the beauty of the tree and the river, which help to make their happiness, are all merged in a story which flows as smoothly and clearly as the river itself.

Mr. Yashima writes with the color and spontaneity of someone to whom English is not just a habit but a living thing. He also writes with the color and integrity of an artist. The pictures themselves, with their warmth and grace, their strength and their richness, are proof of his skill as a painter and as an illustrator for children.

tions in New York, and his work is hung in both private collections and galleries. His illustrations have appeared in *Vogue, Fortune, Harper's* and other magazines. His wife, Mitsu Yashima, is also a painter and illustrator.

The Yashimas have a grown son, Mako, who is studying in New York, and a small daughter, Momo, whose desire to know what her father was like when he was her age brought about *The Village Tree*. Mr. Yashima is a person of depth, vitality, and directness, sensitivity and idealism tempered with practicality and determination.

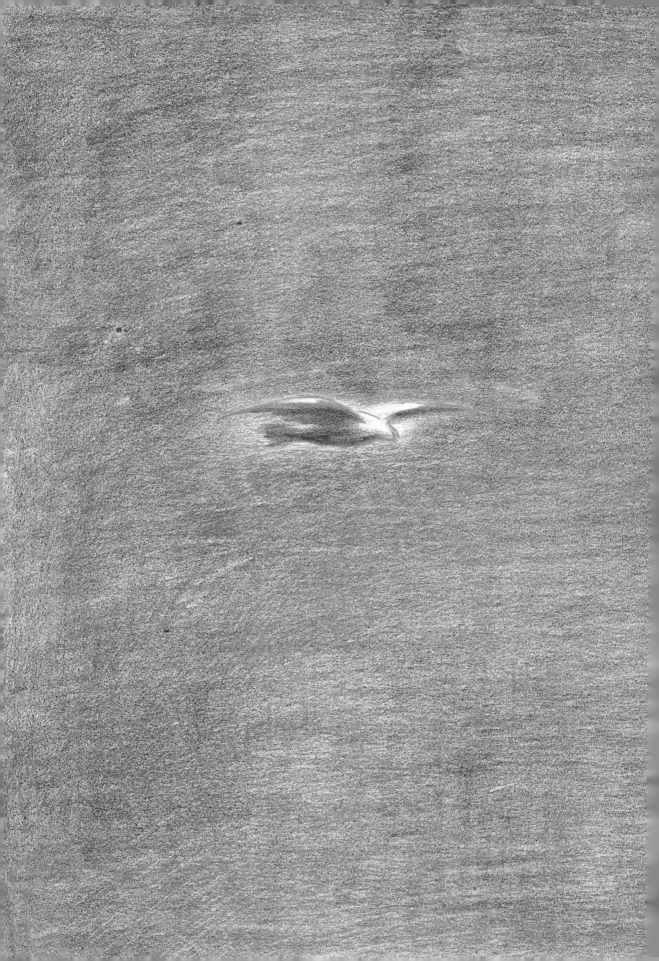

The Village Tree

The Village Tree

村の樹

BY TARO YASHIMA

PUBLISHED BY THE JUNIOR LITERARY GUILD
AND THE VIKING PRESS · NEW YORK
1953

Do you know a country
far, far to the east,
that we call Japan?
Do you know, there too
we have many children
like you?

Copyright 1953 by Taro Yashima. First published by The Viking Press in October 1953. Published on the same day in the Dominion of Canada by The Macmillan Company of Canada Limited. Lithographed in the United States of America by Konecky Associates.

The village where I grew up was on an island far to the south.

A river with plenty of water flowed through the middle of the village, and a huge tree stood on its bank.

As soon as the new summer came, new green leaves came too and began to cover the village, and the river began to float alively.

Early every morning cicadas began to chorus all together on the tree and we children could not stay still at home.

The tree stood stretching out his roots,
some under the ground,
some under the river.
Many branches lifted toward the sky
from his great trunk,
and a few branches
extended low over the river.

We would run to the tree, snatching off our clothes as we ran and tossing them onto bamboo bushes or the grass.

Big children scrambled up the trunk
and climbed to the higher branches.
Smaller children climbed out
on the lower branches.
Babies watched us from the ground.

13

We found all sorts of bugs on the leaves, and places to play
in the branches.

One branch was a swinging pole or a seesaw.

One crotch was a chair. In another crotch we built a house.

Whatever we brought for lunch was so tasty.

When the sun came right above the tree and made us hotter, we jumped into the water.

We all thought up different ways to jump.

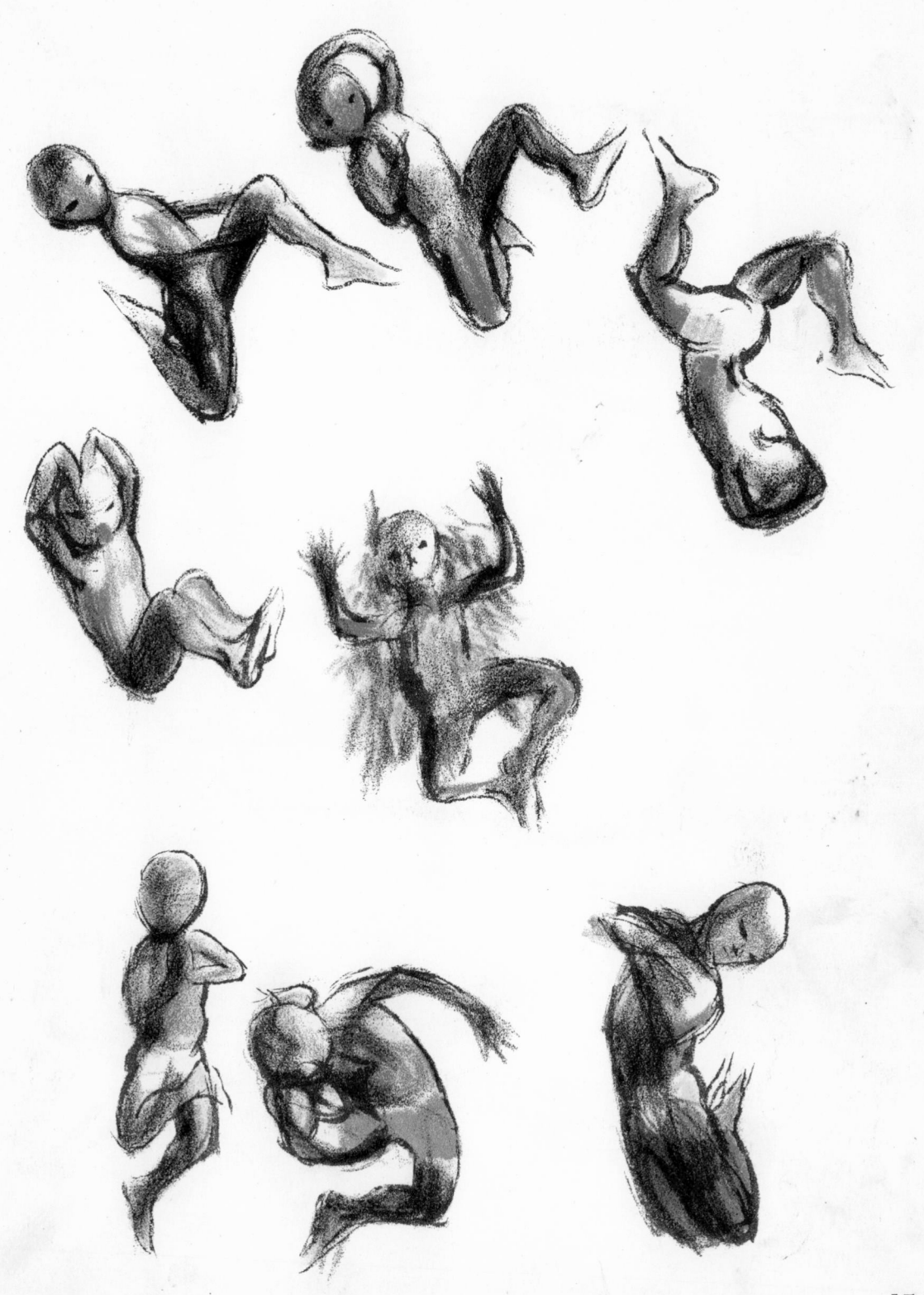

The water was cool and clear, just right for games.

The game to find hidden bamboo leaves was called "Bamboo-Hide."

Finding a stone instead of leaves was called "Stone-Hide."

When a boy dived toward you, saying, "e-e-e!" he looked like a locomotive.

We knocked stones together and the sound *kach-kach-kach-kach* was loud in our ears.

Handstanding and tumbling were much easier to do.

We had a contest to see who could swim farthest under water.

Sometimes grownups came to wash
their horses and gave us a chance
to ride on them.

Even dogs, chickens, and snakes
joined us.

A boy brought down his mother's
washtub and we rowed it in turn.

Large bamboo poles
were wonderful floats.

When we got tired of swimming some of us made a slide by pouring water on the sand bank, making it very wet.

Some of us made things of clay that we found in a secret place in the river bank.

When we got cold, we swam over to the beach across the river.

Here the shallow water was heated by the sun, and we built hot baths
and warmed ourselves.

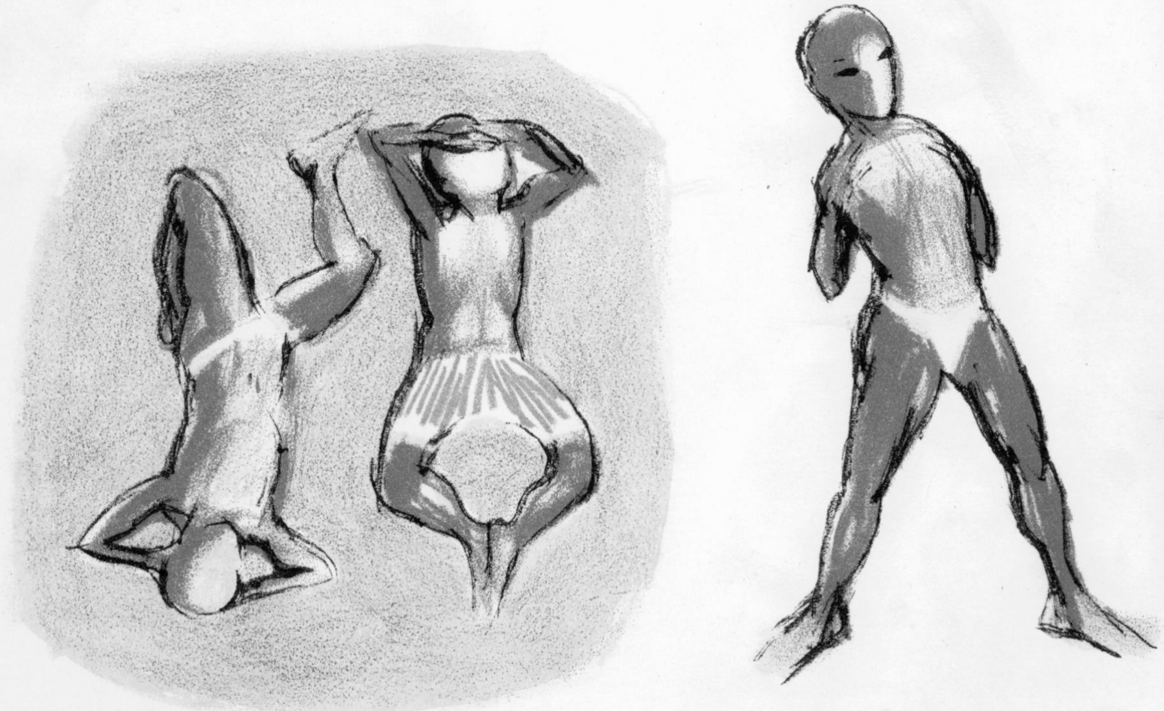

Afterward we lay down flat on heated sand and our bodies were soon dried
and refreshed.

We made puddles of hot water
by scooping up the burning sand
in our hands.

We played wrestling and pole-jumping.

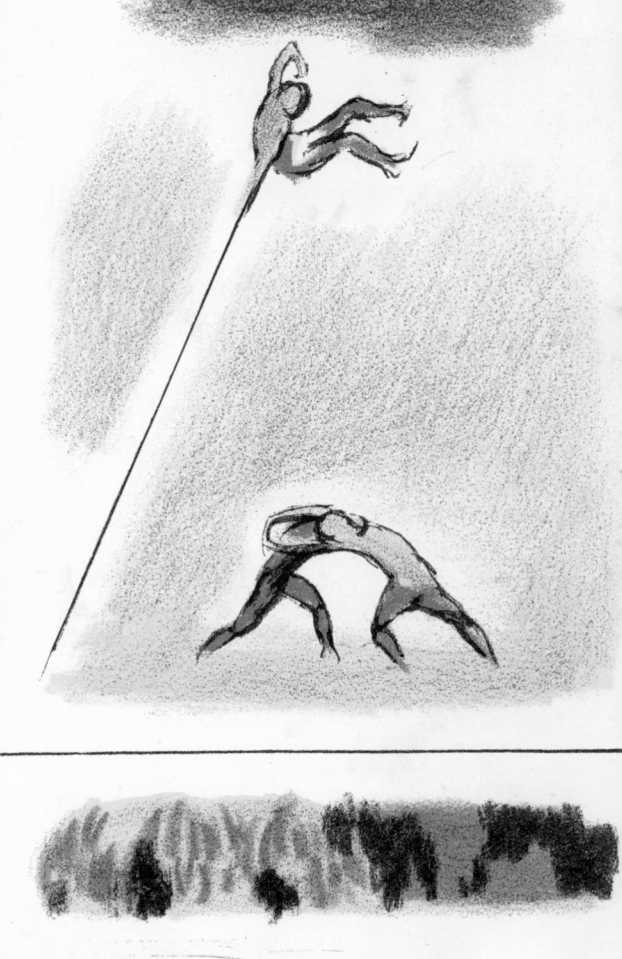

We made crabs and beetles run races.

We skipped stones and threw stones
to see who could throw farthest.   23

Once in a while, grownups came
from the fields nearby to give us watermelons.

Sometimes they brought their calves and colts
to feed in the pasture next to the shore.

Sometimes a man who sold things from village
to village came and told us stories of far places.

Grownups knew how to catch
river fish in many different ways.

There were many kinds of fish in the water.

Shrimps liked the meat of pond-snails
better than anything else.
We caught plenty of shrimps easily
when they came out for eating.

But as soon as the sun went down beyond the hill, the beach was covered with shadow and the water suddenly got cold.

Then all of us swam back across the river to our tree.

27

We dressed in a hurry as our stomachs were empty.

We said to each other, "See you tomorrow?" "Why not!"

When I brought home plenty of shrimps, the supper table became more enjoyable to all the family.

Pig, cat, and chicken liked to eat the shrimps too.

The tree always stood patiently even when no one was around,
just waiting, waiting for the children.

And so the tree stood even when I left the village after I grew up.

They say the tree still stands,
patient and waiting, on the bank.
I can hear the voices of many children
playing the same games
in the same old way.

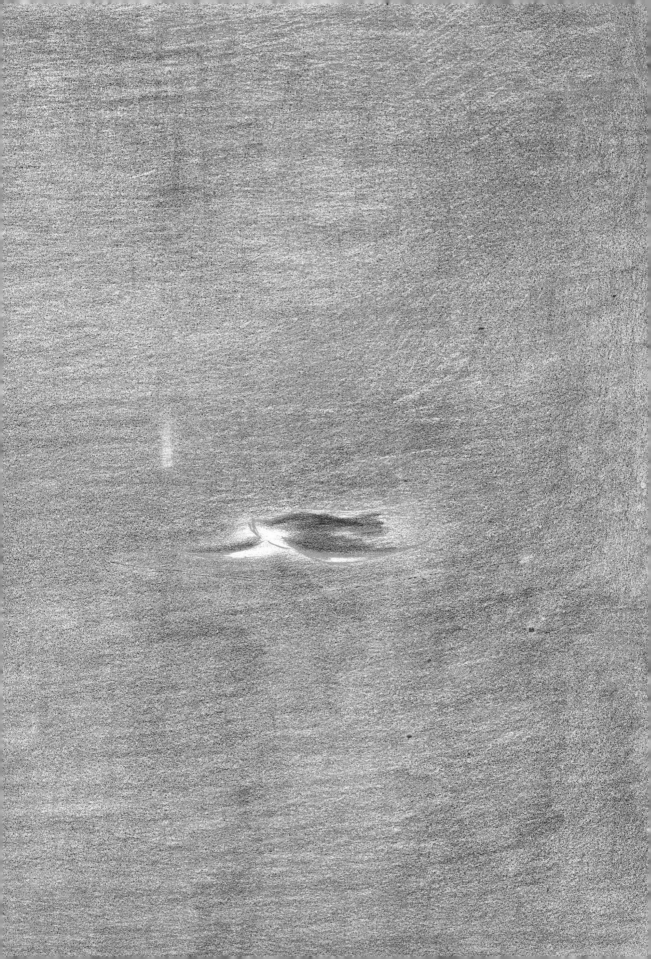

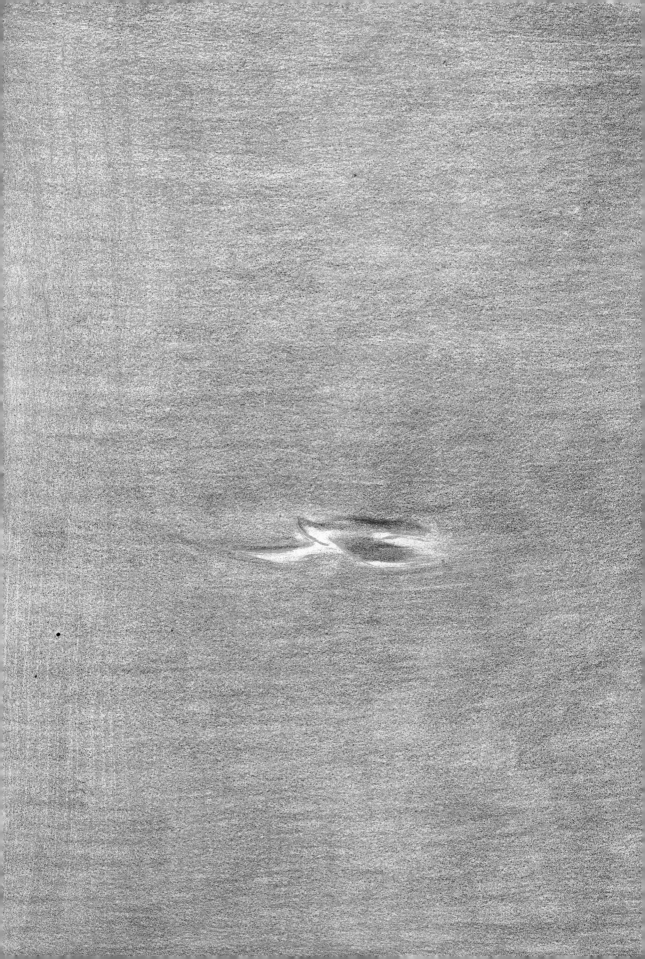